a raven called Charlie

by Molly Burkett
Second Edition

Technical Advisers
Ravenmaster David Cope
Olive Williamson • Roselle Raynes

I.S.B.N Nº 0 - 948204 - 88 - 5

Published by Barny Books • Hough-on-the Hill • Grantham • Lincs
Printed by **TUCANN***design&print* • 19 High Street • Heighington Lincoln LN4 1RG
• Telephone & Fax 01522 790009

The Ravens had nested on the hill side where the ground had fallen away and left a white cut. They had built their nest on a ledge which went two metres back. David and his friends had watched the birds carrying sticks back to the nesting site when the snow was still on the ground. It was a huge nest, taller than either of the birds but when the spring came and the trees were in full leaf, it was difficult to see where the ledge was. It was so well hidden.

The ravens had chosen their nesting site well because it was impossible to see into the nest or get down to it. David had tried. They were noisy birds and the boys often heard them calling or watched first one, then the other, flying lazily in a thermal of air above the hill but they soon dived down if any other bird flew too near their nest site and drove them off. Ravens are strong powerful birds. They are two feet long with a three foot wing span and they are totally black. David knew the young ravens must have hatched when he saw both parents flying together again although they were very busy now, carrying food back to the nest. He saw one of them flying with a grass snake in its beak and he often saw the ravens carrying eggs in the same way.

One evening, the boys were late getting home and they knew they would be in trouble with their parents. It was as they were clambering over a fence that David saw something black hanging on the barbed wire fence at the other end of the field. He reckoned he saw it move and told his friends he was going to see what it was.

"Aw, come on," one of them said. "It's only an old plastic bag blowing in the wind".

But it wasn't. It was a young raven about three quarters grown. Its wing had caught in the point of the barbed wire and the bird had twisted round and round trying to escape. It took David a long time to get the bird free. It was obvious it had hurt its wing.

"I'm taking it across to the coastguards," he told his friends but they wouldn't come with him. They promised to tell his mother why he would be late home.

The coastguards took the young raven and looked after it for a couple of weeks. Then they 'phoned the Tower of London to see if they would like it.

There have always been ravens at the Tower of London for as long as anyone can remember. At one time ravens could be found in the streets of London because they are scavengers and there was plenty for them to find around houses in the middle ages. When Charles the second was King of England, the astrologer complained that the ravens made so much noise, they interfered with his studies. So the

King said that they must be destroyed. But he was told that if the ravens disappeared from the Tower of London, the White Tower would fall and the kingdom with it. So he changed his mind and a limited number were allowed to remain. There are now six ravens at the Tower. They are the official ones and they are listed and draw their rations as if they were soldiers. Then they have two reserve ravens as well. There is a yeoman warder who is the Ravenmaster and he looks after them.

Now the Ravenmaster was pleased when the coastguards 'phoned up and offered him the raven that David had rescued because one of their old birds had died and a young bird was just what he wanted because this bird was young enough to understand and learn the way of the Tower and get to know the other ravens.

At first he was kept in a run on his own so that the other birds could get used to him being there but couldn't get close enough to harm him. When he was allowed out, Charlie did not wander very far from his pen. He soon learned. He copied the other ravens. He came to know which was his territory and he chased any of the other birds out of his area in the same way that he was chased if he went too near theirs.

He soon knew that it was time for food when the Ravenmaster whistled and he knew when it was his turn to go back to his run to be shut up for the night, but it turned out that he wasn't a Charlie at all he was a Charlene. It's difficult to tell the males and females apart. They look so similar although the females are a little heavier than the males but it isn't a reliable way of telling but laying eggs is and that is exactly what Charlie did. She laid an egg, a bluish green egg with brown blotches at one end.

The following year, she paired up with a male raven and they built an enormous nest beside the White Tower but she did not lay any eggs or if she did, the ravens ate them. They tried to nest for several years and then the Ravenmaster built them a special shed where they were hidden away and he gave them lots of sticks to build a nest. They found lots of other things themselves and that nest was built of all sorts of odds and ends that people leave around. There

were lollipop sticks and sweet wrappers, paper bags, cigarette ends and even a child's bobble hat woven in with the twigs. Charlie laid three eggs and one of them hatched. It was the first raven ever to be bred at the Tower. Charlie and Rhys her mate have bred ten more ravens in the following years. Ravens pair for life and certainly these two are very fond of each other. The problem is that Rhys becomes possessive of his mate and can attack the babies so the Ravenmaster takes them away while they are still quite young.

One day Charlie disappeared. Nobody saw her go and for once, Rhys did not seem concerned that she wasn't with him. The Ravenmaster looked everywhere, but there wasn't a sign of her and he began to think that something dreadful must have happened. She couldn't have chosen a worse day to go missing because it was the day of the ceremony when they beat the bounds.

There are several ceremonies that have come down through the ages and beating the bounds is one of them. Years ago when not many people could read or write, they had to put signs in to show where the boundaries were. Well those stones are still in their places around the Tower and once every three years the old practice of beating those bounds takes place and it was the day of that ceremony that Charlie decided to disappear.

The choir and the children were collecting in the church ready for the service which they hold before the parade. Each of the children had a long cane and each time they come to one of the stones, they beat it with the stick. They say that when they started the ceremony years ago they used to beat a boy but now it's the boys that beat the stone. Everything was ready except for Charlie. She should have been shut up in her run but she was nowhere to be seen.

The Ravenmaster said he didn't know what made him go and look outside the grounds just before he went and joined the others at the Church. He knew there was no way the raven could have possibly got out of the gate but he went out to look just the same and you'll never guess what he saw.

There was a soldier standing guard, marching up and down in front of his sentry box at regular intervals. He was in the Welsh Guards and he looked really smart with his red tunic and tall bearskin on his head. He would march ten paces to his right, stamp his feet and march ten paces back and there, following every step he made was Charlie the raven, walking straight behind him lifting up one foot after the other as if she was trying to march as well.

The Ravenmaster didn't stop to ask how long she had been there. He bundled her up and took her back to her pen and shut her up with her mate. He was just in time to join the procession winding its way out of the Tower. It wasn't until later that the Ravenmaster could ask the Welsh Guardsman about the raven and find out how she had got out but it seemed the bird had just fallen into step behind the Guardsman and followed him out. None of the ravens had ever done anything like that before but the Guardsman said,

"Do you remember a raven that came up to the Tower years ago from Anglesey? Only I was the boy that found it tangled up in the barbed wire."

The Ravenmaster looked at him as if he could hardly believe his ears.

"But that is the raven. That was Charlie that followed you out and she's the first raven that has ever had young at the Tower. Didn't you know?"

And the soldier hadn't known but I think the raven had remembered. I think she had known, don't you?